GARFIELD'S
BIG BOOK
OF
EXCELLENT
EXCUSES

by Jim Davis

Written by Mark Acey, Scott Nickel, and Brett Koth
Illustrated by Brett Koth
Designed by Kenny Goetzinger
Additional art support by Mike Fentz, Larry Fentz,
and Lori Barker

SCHOLASTIC INC.

New York Toronto London Auckland Sydney
Mexico City New Delhi Hong Kong Buenos Aires

ISBN 0-439-63910-7

12 11 10 9 8 7 6 5 4 3 2 1   4 5 6 7 8 9/0

Printed in the U.S.A.   40

First Scholastic printing, April 2004

CONTENTS

HOMEWORK HIJINKS

Why I Don't Have My Homework

I was at a rally demanding higher salaries for teachers.

—

The aliens took it back to planet Regoob.

—

I'm allergic to pencil lead.

—

The president called me and yakked all night.

I left my brain
in my locker.

I had a brain cramp.

—

I don't do homework on
days that end in "y."

—

I was being followed to
school by enemy spies,
so I ate it.

—

I got carried away
with my origami
and folded my homework
into a Canada goose.

My dog ate it. Then my science project ate my dog.

Two words:
Cartoon Network.

—

I'm motivationally
challenged.

—

I can't do homework
for medical reasons.
It makes me sick.

—

Oh, you meant *this* week!

I was "visited" by an extraterrestrial, who vaporized my backpack.

Math gives me hives.

—

Isn't homework
considered cruel and
unusual punishment?

—

I forgot to remember.

—

My computer hiccuped.

TARDY HEARTY

Why I'm Not On Time

It's my alarm clock's fault.
It stopped working when I
threw it across the room.

—

I was attacked by a
platoon of army ants.

—

I'm not late...
I'm early for tomorrow.

—

My bike ran out of gas.

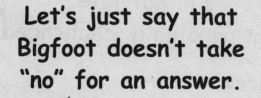

Let's just say that
Bigfoot doesn't take
"no" for an answer.

I'm not late...
I'm punctually challenged.

—

My dog swallowed
my alarm clock.

—

The school bus was attacked
by giant killer tomatoes.
You didn't see it?
It was on the news.

—

I couldn't jump-start
my alarm clock.

I fell in a puddle
of dog drool.

It's my parents' fault.
I'm genetically predisposed
to tardiness.

—

I was trying to get the
static cling out of my socks.

—

We have a really old toaster
that takes a long time to
warm up in the mornings.

—

A thirsty hippo was hogging
the water fountain.

OUT OF SIGHT

Why I Was Absent

I have a note from
my doctor.

—

I have a note from
my mother.

—

I have a note from
my doctor's mother.

—

I was there,
but I was invisible.

Two words:
alien abduction!

My goldfish died, and I
was burying him at sea.

—

My hair hurt.

—

I had "student's flu."
(I was sick of school.)

—

I was staging a sit-in to
protest too much homework.

I was in a tree
hanging out with possums.

I was watering
my Chia pet.

—

I'm too cool to care.

—

I couldn't miss
my yodeling lesson.

—

You mean we don't get
Groundhog Day off?

I was undercover.

My marmoset
ran away from home.

—

I was visiting relatives
on my home planet.

—

My pet ant died,
and I was grieving.

—

I was time-traveling.

DATING DODGES

Why I Can't Go Out with You

Because I'll be washing
my hair all that week.
Each one, individually.

—

I don't date outside
my species.

—

I have to pick up my
wombat from the
taxidermist that night.

—

I'm a strict observer of
national "Don't Date a
Loser" week.

Sorry, but that's my night
to floss the dog.

I have an
important engagement
at Buckingham Palace.

—

It's too dangerous. I might
yawn myself to death.

—

Two words:
terminal geekitis.

—

I just remembered—
I'm married.

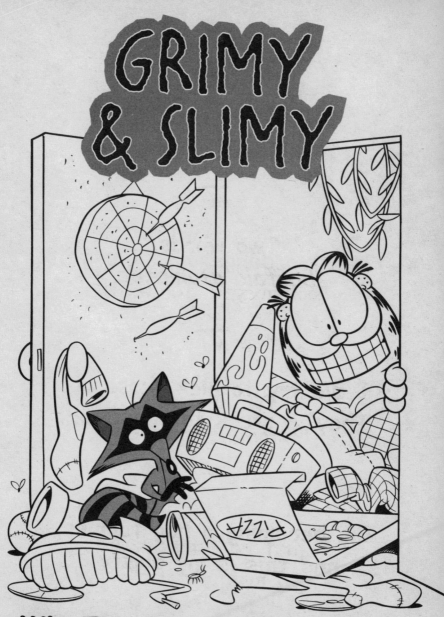

Rowdy raccoons
ransacked my room!

—

Two words:
buffalo stampede!

—

I *did* try to pick those up.
They're stuck to the floor.

—

I'm becoming a hog farmer,
and this is my pigsty.

I was frightened
at an early age
by a vacuum
cleaner.

I can't clean without
a court order.

—

Doing chores gives
me a rash.

—

I'm trying to create
the world's largest
indoor landfill.

—

I'm allergic to cleanliness.

Broom handles... splinters...
coincidence? I think not.

Have you taken a deep
breath? That dirty sock
is an air freshener.

—

My doctor won't let me
lift anything heavier than
the remote control.

—

It's a union job,
and I'm not a member.

—

But I already cleaned
last year.

FOOD ATTITUDE

Why I Won't Eat Something

Sorry, I'm
vegetable-intolerant.

—

"Squash" is not a vegetable...
it's a verb.

—

I'm on an all-candy diet.

—

I think it's still breathing.

Octopus is an acquired
taste—one I have no
intention of acquiring.

I'm on a hunger strike to
protest too much homework.

—

Because I tried to sneak
it to the dog, and even he
wouldn't touch it.

—

There's not enough
sugar in it.

—

I don't eat anything
with a face.

Sorry,
but for
me to eat
that would
take more
ketchup
than we
have in
the house.

Give it to Popeye.
I don't do spinach.

—

Leftovers are okay, but
not from the Civil War.

—

Because I'm still
traumatized by those turnips
you fed me last week.

—

Casserole... Isn't that
French for "yuck"?

Why I'm Still on the Phone

I can't just hang up on
the president, can I?

—

I'm calling
1-800-I-LUV-MATH.

—

I'm telling everyone what
a way cool parent you are.

—

It's *not* "spending too
much time on the phone"...
it's "networking."

What can I
say? I'm a
"yakkasaurus."

45

I'm preparing for a career
as a telemarketer.

—

If I'm the 212th lucky
caller, I have a chance
to win a T-shirt!

—

I'm trying to set a new
world's record.

—

You know, my Psychic Friend
predicted you'd be upset
about the phone bill.

Would you believe the receiver's stuck to my head again?

I found a guy in France
to help tutor me in French.
Isn't that cool?

—

I'm in the middle
of a heated discussion
about punctuation.

—

You *said* you wanted
me to spend more time
with Grandma.

—

Because it's cheaper to call
New Zealand than fly there.

SLOW CASH FLOW

Why I Need a Bigger Allowance

My piggy bank went
bankrupt.

—

Then I can afford
to get that huge
flaming-skull tattoo!

—

My broker called.
The market for pork
bellies is hot right now.

—

I'm buying a summer home.

My skateboard
needs an oil change.

I have a lot of overhead.

—

Inflation is killing me.

—

Because a child of a
wonderful parent like you
deserves only the best.

—

I want to put it
into my college fund.
Yeah, that's it.

**For food. I'm training
to be a sumo wrestler.**

Would you believe I'm
giving it all to charity?

—

Because you have to have
money to make money.

—

My pet iguana needs
a special operation.

—

I'm making a big
campaign contribution.

The court is too small
for my enormous talent.

—

The earth's magnetic
field disrupted the flight
of the ball.

—

The refs hated
our uniforms.

—

I didn't want to make
the other team look bad.

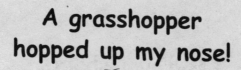

A grasshopper
hopped up my nose!

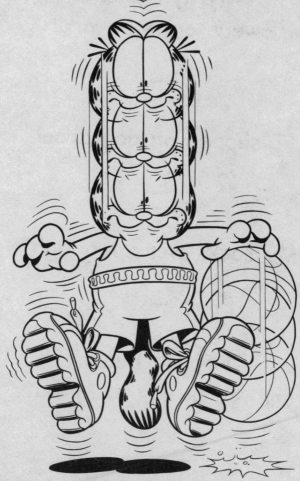

My gym shorts
were on backward!

—

I slipped on dog drool.

—

My socks were too tight.

—

A rogue beaver
chewed up my lucky bat.

It's not me,
it's this
cheap equipment.

I was trying too hard to
impress all the pro scouts
who flocked here to see me.

—

I lost track of the ball
when I started reading my
opponent's tattoos!

—

The field was wet,
which canceled out
my tremendous speed.

—

I tripped on a gopher.

I'm still bummed out over Michael Jordan's retirement.

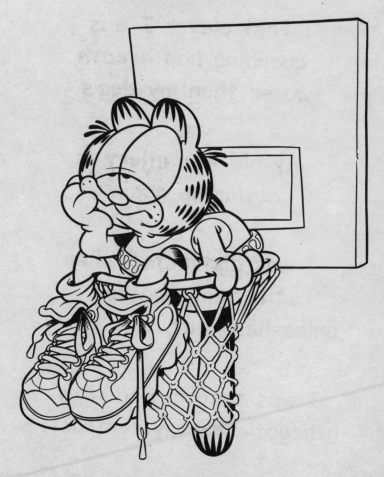

I'm saving my energy
for when I turn pro.

—

That player I was
guarding had breath
worse than my dog's.

—

My old war injury is
acting up again.

—

I was distracted when
the team mascot
unleashed that huge burp.

—

I was preoccupied with
renegotiating my contract.

I tripped on a hair ball.

—

My cat was surfing
the 'Net all night.

—

I ate too much sugar.

—

I'm goofy from watching
too much TV.

I'm having a bad hair day.

My water bed
made me seasick.

—

There was a postal
mix-up, and I was mailed
to Abu Dhabi.

—

I got a wedgie.

—

My cat's snoring kept
me up all night.

I was too busy
doing nothing.

I was just following
the recipe!

—

My brain wasn't getting
enough blood because my
underwear was too tight.

—

I had my contact lenses
in backward.

—

I was in Uruguay
at the time.

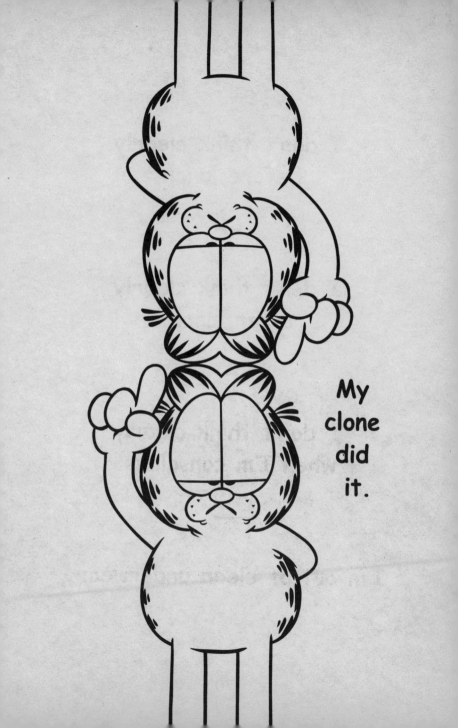

My
clone
did
it.

I don't think clearly
before lunch.

—

I don't think clearly
after lunch.

—

I don't think clearly
when I'm conscious.

—

I'm out of clean underwear.

That was a left-brained task,
and I'm a right-brained person.

Tiny gnomes came
in the middle of the
night and did it.

—

I was alphabetizing
my sock drawer.

—

You didn't say "Pretty please
with sugar on top."

—

It's all part of a big
government conspiracy.

I was up all night
housebreaking my pet flea.

My tuna burrito
backed up on me.

—

Boy, time sure flies,
doesn't it?

—

I got my tongue stuck
to a Popsicle.

—

The Psychic Hotline
advised against it.

My
super-
powers
failed
me
again.

My brain got sucked
into the TV.

—

In the great scheme of
things, is this really
all that important?

—

That runs counter to every
belief I've ever held dear.

—

I'm overly susceptible
to advertising.

It's still on "back order."

That offends
my sensibilities.

—

I don't make the rules;
I just follow them.

—

That's not my department.

—

I was busy
thinking up excuses.

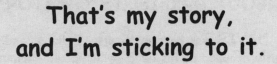

That's my story, and I'm sticking to it.

DEPARTMENT OF EXCUSES

ABOUT GARFIELD'S CREATOR

JIM DAVIS was born in Marion, Indiana, and was promptly dropped on his head—which could explain his lifelong desire to be a cartoonist. Jim still lives in the Hoosier state, preferring the quiet joys of life in the country, where a man can walk his pig in peace.

ABOUT THE AUTHORS

MARK ACEY grew up in Cincinnati, dreaming of playing second base for the Reds. But finding he was better at wordplay than the double play, he became a humor writer. Today Mark lives in Indianapolis with his wife, Jugnoo, dreaming up excuses for not doing yard work ("An evil squirrel stole my rake!").

Reared in Los Angeles, **SCOTT NICKEL** has seen it all and done it all—and remembers surprisingly little of it. Scott is a dedicated wordsmith and dreams of someday writing the perfect knock-knock joke. He currently lives in Indiana with his wife, two sons, three dogs, one cat, a cockatiel, and several sea monkeys.

BRETT KOTH is a teeny-tiny cartoonist with a big fat desire to entertain. He and his lovely wife, Mona, live in a thimble in sunny Orlando, Florida, where he moonlights as a singing cabana boy. Brett's hobbies include reading, jazz, baseball, and playing traditional folk songs on his armpit.